World Tales

The Frog Emperor

A Chinese tale told by Anne Adeney

Illustrated by Natascia Ugliano

FRANKLIN WATTS
LONDON•SYDNEY

First published in 2009 by
Franklin Watts
338 Euston Road
London
NW1 3BH

Franklin Watts Australia
Level 17/207 Kent Street
Sydney
NSW 2000

Text © Anne Adeney 2009
Illustration © Natascia Ugliano 2009

The rights of Anne Adeney to be identified as the author
and Natascia Ugliano as the illustrator of this Work have
been asserted in accordance with the Copyright, Designs
and Patents Act, 1988.

All rights reserved. No part of this publication may be
reproduced, stored in a retrieval system, or transmitted
in any form or by any means, electronic, mechanical,
photocopy, recording or otherwise, without the prior
written permission of the copyright owner.

A CIP catalogue record for this book is available
from the British Library.

ISBN 978 0 7496 8596 6 (hbk)
ISBN 978 0 7496 8602 4 (pbk)

Series Editor: Jackie Hamley
Series Advisor: Dr Barrie Wade
Series Designer: Peter Scoulding

Printed in China

Franklin Watts is a division of
Hachette Children's Books,
an Hachette UK company.
www.hachette.co.uk

This tale comes from
China. Can you find
China on a map?

Long ago, a poor couple
had a son called Ju-Long.

He was a beautiful
baby frog!

When Ju-Long was older,

a war broke out in China.

One day, Ju-Long said,
"Take me to the Emperor.
I can win the war!"

Ju-Long's father took him
to the Emperor's palace.

There was a notice on the palace gates.

The man who wins
the war shall marry
my daughter,
the princess.

Signed
The Emperor

The enemies were nearly
at the city walls and the
Emperor was afraid.

9

"My son, Ju-Long, can win
this war," said the father.

"How? He is just a big frog!" the Emperor laughed.

"I need hot coals," Ju-Long explained. "When I have eaten them, you must open the palace gates."

12

"But our enemies will rush in!" cried the Emperor.

"Yes, and I will beat them," said Ju-Long.

The Emperor had to
agree with Ju-Long's plan.

Ju-Long ate plates of hot
coals for three days.

15

On the third day, he gave a sign for the soldiers to open the palace gates.

The enemies rushed to the gates. Ju-Long spat fire on them until they ran away.

The Emperor was happy, but he didn't want a frog son. "My daughter cannot marry a frog!

Only the man who can catch this ball will marry the princess!" he declared. Ju-Long hopped away.

A handsome young man
jumped and caught the ball.

He and the princess got
married that afternoon.

But the handsome young
man was really Ju-Long.

Only the princess knew
that he could take off his
frog skin.

Soon the Emperor found
out. "Why do you wear
that frog skin?" he asked.

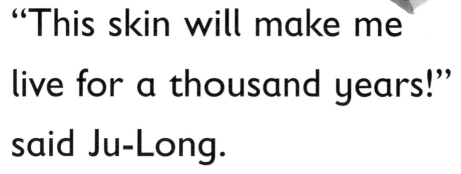

"This skin will make me
live for a thousand years!"
said Ju-Long.

"Give it to me!" ordered the Emperor.

As the Emperor put on the frog skin, Ju-Long smiled.

Ju-Long became the new
Emperor ...

... but the old Emperor stayed a frog forever!

Puzzle 1

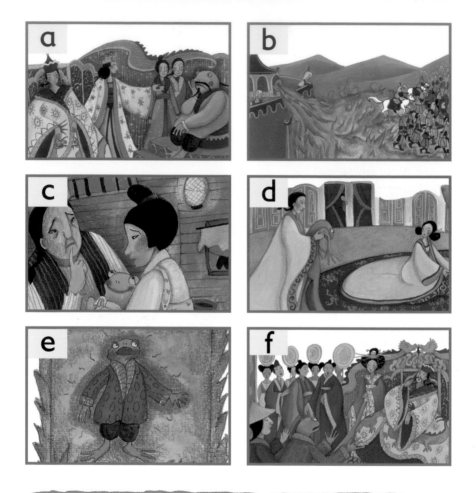

Put these pictures in the correct order.
Now tell the story in your own words.
What different endings can you think of?

Puzzle 2

brave   wise
frightened

bold   unfair
kind

scary   nasty
gentle

Choose the correct adjectives for each character. Which adjectives are incorrect? Turn over to find the answers.

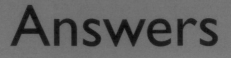

Answers

Puzzle 1

The correct order is: 1c, 2f, 3e, 4b, 5d, 6a

Puzzle 2

Ju-Long: the correct adjectives are brave, wise

The incorrect adjective is frightened

The Emperor: the correct adjective is unfair

The incorrect adjectives are bold, kind

The princess: the correct adjective is gentle

The incorrect adjectives are nasty, scary

Look out for Leapfrog fairy tales:

For more Leapfrog books go to: www.franklinwatts.co.uk